D1017440

WHY YOU'RE SO AWESOME

Your

---

is totally awesome.

You are the most awesome

_____

in the world.

You have the funniest

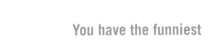

4

You are awesomely
talented at

_____ .

It would have been awesome
to know you when

_____ .

If you were a holiday, you'd be

_____ .

7

It's awesome going to

_____

with you.

I wish I were as awesome as you at

_____ .

I want to steal your awesome

10

We'd make an awesome

---

team.

11

It is awesome how you

_____ .

12

You deserve the Awesome

Award.

13

Your

_____

should be studied by science.

14

You're awesome at giving

_____ .

15

If you wanted to, you could easily

_____ .

16

You have awesome taste in

——————————————————————————— .

17

It's awesome how you

_____

every day.

18

If you were an animal, you'd be

_____ .

19

You make me want to be a more awesome

_____ .

20

It's awesome how you're
usually right about

_____ .

21

I wish I knew your secret for

_____ .

It would be awesome to see you

_____ .

23

People seem to be impressed with
your awesome

_____ .

24

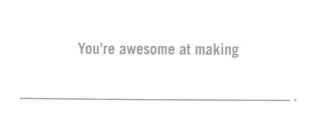

You're awesome at making

——————————————————————————————— .

Everyone should be as awesomely

_____

as you.

It would be awesome if you would never

_____

again.

27

It's awesome to play

---

with you.

I believe the world needs your
uniquely awesome

_____ .

_____

should play you in the movie of your life.

It's awesome that you get my

_____ .

31

We should totally

---

someday.

32

It's awesome how you want to

_____ .

33

I still can't get over how you

_____ .

34

It's awesome how you keep getting better at

_____ .

35

If we could bottle your

_____

and sell it, we'd make a fortune.

36

It is so awesomely funny when you

_____ .

37

I am eternally grateful that you

_____ .

It's awesome how you have such strong

_____ .

If you were a color, you'd be

_____.

Remember how awesome it was when

_____ ?

It's awesome when you

_____

like

_____ .

I never get bored of your

_____ .

It would be awesome to go to

_____

with you.

I can't wait to see what happens when

_____ .

45

I am slightly obsessed with your awesome

_____ .

I always want to hear what you're
going to say about

_____ .

47

It's awesome how you
believe in

_____ .

48

If you were a junk food item,
you'd be

_____ .

49

Nobody is as awesome as you at

_____ .

I am so

_____

that

_____ .

Created, published, and distributed by Knock Knock
6080 Center Drive
Los Angeles, CA 90045
knockknockstuff.com
Knock Knock is a registered trademark of Knock Knock LLC
Fill in the Love is a registered trademark of Knock Knock LLC
© 2013 Knock Knock LLC
All rights reserved
Made in China

UPC: 825703-50063-9   ISBN: 978-160106547-6

31

#fillinthelove